"Why fit in when you were born to stand out?"
– Dr. Suess

Aunt Phil's Trunk

31 Journal Prompts
Kids' **Self-Discovery**
Ages 8-12

By
Laurel Downing Bill

Aunt Phil's Trunk LLC, Anchorage, Alaska
www.AuntPhilsTrunk.com

International Standard Book Number: 978-1-940479-92-7
Printed and bound in the United States of America

An Introduction to Journaling

Daily journaling is a wonderful habit that can transform your life if you let it. For the next 31 days, you're invited on a journey to discover who you are, explore new dreams and design your next big adventure into the writing realm.

Journaling works best when you create room for it in your life. Some people prefer to journal first thing in the morning so they can start their days feeling energized. Others prefer the quiet of early afternoons or late nights. Choose a time that feels right to you and set aside 20-30 minutes to write your thoughts.

In this journal, you'll find 31 prompts to inspire your inner self. You can work through the prompts in chronological order – or if you prefer, skip around. Open the journal to a random page. Pick a topic that appeals to you and go for it.

Keep in mind that your journal is a judgement-free zone. It's OK if you misspell a word, use a run-on sentence, or even forget punctuation altogether. You're not writing to impress others or earn an "A" on your report card. You're writing for yourself and you're the only one that will ever read these words.

So, give yourself the freedom to explore, to play and to create within these pages.

Planning New Adventures

Every day brings potential for new works to flow from your pen! Use the questions in this journaling book to help you jump-start your new stories.

You also can take this journaling process a step further to help you come up with ideas for more projects. Write down observations/events/conversations you observe during your day.

Then jot down ideas that may come to mind from your journal entries and observations.

1. Which season is better, winter or summer? Write down why you chose that season.

_____

_____

_____

_____

_____

_____

_____

_____

_____

_____

_____

_____

_____

_____

_____

_____

_____

_____

Observations of the day:

_____

_____

_____

_____

_____

_____

_____

_____

_____

Story ideas:

_____

_____

_____

_____

_____

_____

_____

_____

2. If someone gave you $1,000, what would you buy and why?

_____

_____

_____

_____

_____

_____

_____

_____

_____

_____

_____

_____

_____

_____

_____

_____

_____

_____

_____

_____

Observations of the day:

_____

_____

_____

_____

_____

_____

_____

_____

_____

Story ideas:

_____

_____

_____

_____

_____

_____

_____

_____

3. What do you want be when you grow up and why?

_____

_____

_____

_____

_____

_____

_____

_____

_____

_____

_____

_____

_____

_____

_____

_____

_____

_____

Observations of the day:

_____

_____

_____

_____

_____

_____

_____

_____

_____

_____

Story ideas:

_____

_____

_____

_____

_____

_____

_____

_____

_____

4. Who is your favorite person on the planet? What do you like most about that person?

_____

_____

_____

_____

_____

_____

_____

_____

_____

_____

_____

_____

_____

_____

_____

_____

_____

_____

_____

Observations of the day:

_____

_____

_____

_____

_____

_____

_____

_____

_____

_____

Story ideas:

_____

_____

_____

_____

_____

_____

_____

_____

5. Write about a time you felt really happy. What happened? What made you feel happy?

_____

_____

_____

_____

_____

_____

_____

_____

_____

_____

_____

_____

_____

_____

_____

_____

_____

_____

Observations of the day:

_____

_____

_____

_____

_____

_____

_____

_____

_____

_____

Story ideas:

_____

_____

_____

_____

_____

_____

_____

_____

_____

6. If you were in charge of the whole world, what would you do to make the world a happier place?

_____

_____

_____

_____

_____

_____

_____

_____

_____

_____

_____

_____

_____

_____

_____

_____

_____

_____

Observations of the day:

_____

_____

_____

_____

_____

_____

_____

_____

_____

_____

Story ideas:

_____

_____

_____

_____

_____

_____

_____

_____

_____

7. What are some of your favorite animals? What do you like about them?

_____

_____

_____

_____

_____

_____

_____

_____

_____

_____

_____

_____

_____

_____

_____

_____

_____

_____

_____

Observations of the day:

_____

_____

_____

_____

_____

_____

_____

_____

_____

Story ideas:

_____

_____

_____

_____

_____

_____

_____

8. Write about your favorite sport and why you like it so much.

_____

_____

_____

_____

_____

_____

_____

_____

_____

_____

_____

_____

_____

_____

_____

_____

_____

_____

_____

_____

Observations of the day:

_____

_____

_____

_____

_____

_____

_____

_____

_____

Story ideas:

_____

_____

_____

_____

_____

_____

_____

_____

A professional writer is an amateur who didn't quit.

— Richard Bach

9. If you had one wish, what would it be?

_____

_____

_____

_____

_____

_____

_____

_____

_____

_____

_____

_____

_____

_____

_____

_____

_____

_____

_____

_____

Observations of the day:

_____

_____

_____

_____

_____

_____

_____

_____

_____

_____

Story ideas:

_____

_____

_____

_____

_____

_____

_____

_____

10. What was one of your favorite toys when you were little? Do you still enjoy playing with it?

Observations of the day:

_____

_____

_____

_____

_____

_____

_____

_____

_____

Story ideas:

_____

_____

_____

_____

_____

_____

_____

_____

11. What is your favorite holiday and why?

_____

_____

_____

_____

_____

_____

_____

_____

_____

_____

_____

_____

_____

_____

_____

_____

_____

_____

_____

_____

Observations of the day:

_____

_____

_____

_____

_____

_____

_____

_____

_____

Story ideas:

_____

_____

_____

_____

_____

_____

_____

_____

12. What is a food you hate? Write about it!

_____

_____

_____

_____

_____

_____

_____

_____

_____

_____

_____

_____

_____

_____

_____

_____

_____

_____

_____

Observations of the day:

_____

_____

_____

_____

_____

_____

_____

_____

_____

_____

Story ideas:

_____

_____

_____

_____

_____

_____

_____

_____

13. If you could be any animal, which one would you be and why?

_____

_____

_____

_____

_____

_____

_____

_____

_____

_____

_____

_____

_____

_____

_____

_____

_____

_____

Observations of the day:

_____

_____

_____

_____

_____

_____

_____

_____

_____

_____

Story ideas:

_____

_____

_____

_____

_____

_____

_____

_____

_____

14. Is it a good idea to keep ALL secrets a secret? Write about examples of when it is okay to spill a secret – and when it isn't okay.

_____

_____

_____

_____

_____

_____

_____

_____

_____

_____

_____

_____

_____

_____

_____

_____

_____

_____

_____

_____

Observations of the day:

_____

_____

_____

_____

_____

_____

_____

_____

_____

Story ideas:

_____

_____

_____

_____

_____

_____

_____

_____

15. Is there something you are good at doing? Write about your best strengths.

_____

_____

_____

_____

_____

_____

_____

_____

_____

_____

_____

_____

_____

_____

_____

_____

_____

_____

Observations of the day:

_____

_____

_____

_____

_____

_____

_____

_____

_____

_____

Story ideas:

_____

_____

_____

_____

_____

_____

_____

_____

_____

16. Write about five things you can do that are important for you to stay healthy and safe.

_____

_____

_____

_____

_____

_____

_____

_____

_____

_____

_____

_____

_____

_____

_____

_____

_____

_____

_____

_____

Observations of the day:

_____

_____

_____

_____

_____

_____

_____

_____

_____

_____

Story ideas:

_____

_____

_____

_____

_____

_____

_____

_____

Let Today Be the Start of Something New

17. What would you most like to learn over the next year? Think about things that interest you and make a list!

_____

_____

_____

_____

_____

_____

_____

_____

_____

_____

_____

_____

_____

_____

_____

_____

_____

_____

_____

Observations of the day:

_____

_____

_____

_____

_____

_____

_____

_____

_____

Story ideas:

_____

_____

_____

_____

_____

_____

_____

_____

18. What are some ways you can start up a conversation with someone you have never met before?

_____

_____

_____

_____

_____

_____

_____

_____

_____

_____

_____

_____

_____

_____

_____

_____

_____

_____

_____

Observations of the day:

_____

_____

_____

_____

_____

_____

_____

_____

_____

_____

Story ideas:

_____

_____

_____

_____

_____

_____

_____

_____

19. Are there any chores you have to do at home? What are they? What do you like – and not like – about each one?

_____

_____

_____

_____

_____

_____

_____

_____

_____

_____

_____

_____

_____

_____

_____

_____

_____

_____

_____

Observations of the day:

_____

_____

_____

_____

_____

_____

_____

_____

_____

Story ideas:

_____

_____

_____

_____

_____

_____

_____

_____

20. Write a list of 10 things you can do to practice kindness to others.

_____

_____

_____

_____

_____

_____

_____

_____

_____

_____

_____

_____

_____

_____

_____

_____

_____

_____

_____

Observations of the day:

_____

_____

_____

_____

_____

_____

_____

_____

_____

Story ideas:

_____

_____

_____

_____

_____

_____

_____

_____

21. Is there a homework subject you dread? Why do you not like getting homework in that subject?

_____

_____

_____

_____

_____

_____

_____

_____

_____

_____

_____

_____

_____

_____

_____

_____

_____

_____

_____

_____

Observations of the day:

_____

_____

_____

_____

_____

_____

_____

_____

_____

Story ideas:

_____

_____

_____

_____

_____

_____

_____

_____

22. What scares you? What helps you to feel less afraid? What would you say to a friend who fears something to help them feel less afraid?

_____

_____

_____

_____

_____

_____

_____

_____

_____

_____

_____

_____

_____

_____

_____

_____

_____

_____

_____

_____

_____

Observations of the day:

_____

_____

_____

_____

_____

_____

_____

_____

_____

_____

Story ideas:

_____

_____

_____

_____

_____

_____

_____

_____

_____

23. Write a letter to your future self in 20 years.

_____

_____

_____

_____

_____

_____

_____

_____

_____

_____

_____

_____

_____

_____

_____

_____

_____

_____

Observations of the day:

_____

_____

_____

_____

_____

_____

_____

_____

_____

Story ideas:

_____

_____

_____

_____

_____

_____

_____

_____

24. In addition to basic survival needs such as food, water, air and shelter, what are three things you wouldn't want to live without? Why?

_____

_____

_____

_____

_____

_____

_____

_____

_____

_____

_____

_____

_____

_____

_____

_____

_____

_____

_____

_____

Observations of the day:

_____

_____

_____

_____

_____

_____

_____

_____

_____

Story ideas:

_____

_____

_____

_____

_____

_____

_____

_____

25. Do you want to go to college? Why or why not?

Observations of the day:

_____

_____

_____

_____

_____

_____

_____

_____

_____

Story ideas:

_____

_____

_____

_____

_____

_____

_____

_____

*I can shake off everything as
I write; my sorrows disappear,
my courage is reborn.*

– Anne Frank

26. Would you rather have a goldfish or shark as a pet? Why?

_____

_____

_____

_____

_____

_____

_____

_____

_____

_____

_____

_____

_____

_____

_____

_____

_____

_____

_____

_____

Observations of the day:

_____

_____

_____

_____

_____

_____

_____

_____

Story ideas:

_____

_____

_____

_____

_____

_____

_____

_____

27. If you could meet any famous person today, who would you want to meet and why? What questions might you ask him or her?

_____

_____

_____

_____

_____

_____

_____

_____

_____

_____

_____

_____

_____

_____

_____

_____

_____

_____

_____

Observations of the day:

_____

_____

_____

_____

_____

_____

_____

_____

_____

_____

Story ideas:

_____

_____

_____

_____

_____

_____

_____

_____

28. What does the word courage mean to you?

_____

_____

_____

_____

_____

_____

_____

_____

_____

_____

_____

_____

_____

_____

_____

_____

_____

_____

_____

_____

_____

_____

Observations of the day:

_____

_____

_____

_____

_____

_____

_____

_____

_____

Story ideas:

_____

_____

_____

_____

_____

_____

_____

_____

_____

29. What makes you unique? What are some of your strengths? What are some of your weaknesses?

_____

_____

_____

_____

_____

_____

_____

_____

_____

_____

_____

_____

_____

_____

_____

_____

_____

_____

Observations of the day:

_____

_____

_____

_____

_____

_____

_____

_____

_____

Story ideas:

_____

_____

_____

_____

_____

_____

_____

_____

30. What can you do to set a good example for others to be kind?

_____

_____

_____

_____

_____

_____

_____

_____

_____

_____

_____

_____

_____

_____

_____

_____

_____

Observations of the day:

_____

_____

_____

_____

_____

_____

_____

_____

_____

_____

Story ideas:

_____

_____

_____

_____

_____

_____

_____

_____

31. A credo is a statement of personal beliefs. Try writing your own credo of things that you believe in and feel are important.

_____

_____

_____

_____

_____

_____

_____

_____

_____

_____

_____

_____

_____

_____

_____

_____

_____

_____

_____

_____

_____

Observations of the day:

_____

_____

_____

_____

_____

_____

_____

_____

_____

Story ideas:

_____

_____

_____

_____

_____

_____

_____

_____

Don't tell me the moon is shining; show me the glint of light on broken glass.

– Anton Chekhov

Made in the USA
Columbia, SC
06 June 2021